Funny Face

by Lindsay menson

illustrated by John Yahyeh

Characters

Me, Lisa

Chloe

Ben

"Lisa!" yells Dad. He's seen me in the rear-vision mirror.

I am so busted. Dad stops the car. "Chloe, get in the back. Lisa, move down the front with me."

Chapter 3

Ace Face

I climb in the front with Dad and Mum gets in the middle with Ben. I look back at Ace. Chloe gives me a wave and a smile. Then I see Ace jumping around, barking madly. He can smell the garbage truck in the next lane. Ace loves garbage. He's trying to climb out the window, but Chloe holds him back.

Chloe winds up the window. Ace squishes his nose to the glass. Ace is doing doggie, funny faces!

"What a dog!" I yell proudly.

"Sit down!" yells Chloe.

"Stupid dog," yells Dad as he passes the garbage truck.

There is dog slobber all over the windows, the seats and Chloe. "Stop the car!" yells Chloe. "I can't sit with this dog anymore."

Dad stops the car. "Swap seats with your mother."

Mum and Chloe swap seats. This is bad. How am I going to pull funny faces now? I rack my brain for an idea, but Ben comes up with a brilliant solution. He throws up! Bits of green bean and orange carrot fly everywhere.

"I'm going to be sick too!" screeches Chloe.

"Check out those colours," I gasp.

Dad pulls the car over again. It takes ages to clean up the mess. When it's time to go again Mum says, "I think I should sit with Ben."

Chloe wants to sit up the front with Dad. Dad breathes a heavy sigh and nods. He looks at Ace and me. "OK you two, in the back."

Ace and I try to hide our excitement. We are back in the funny face seat!

Chapter 4

Face Off

Dad keeps looking at me through the rear-vision mirror. I play it cool for a little while and take a funny face break.

Suddenly Ace and I see the Happy Village minibus coming up behind us. The driver gives us a wave, changes lane and drives along beside us. We can hardly believe our eyes.

Every person on the bus is pulling a face!
They are the most wicked funny faces I have
ever seen. There are squashed faces, pushed
faces, pressed, squished and pulled faces.

"Ahhhhhhhhh," Chloe sees the bus and lets
out a huge scream.

"What on earth?" cries Mum.

Ben points and laughs, "Funny face! Funny
face!"

"What do they want?" asks Chloe.

"I know what they want!" I cry. "They want a face off!" I pull a face. "Try and beat that one!" I yell. The whole bus comes back at me with my super-fish-face. I am so mad. That is my funny face — not anyone else's! "They stole my face!" I yell. "Hey that's my face you're pulling! Get your own!"

"Stop shouting, Lisa!" yells Dad.

"But they stole my face!" I protest.

"Try and lose them," says Mum.

Dad weaves through traffic. Suddenly there are flashing lights and sirens. "It's the police," whispers Chloe. Dad slows down and pulls over.

Chapter 5

Funny Face

The policeman looks at Dad. "You seem to be in a bit of a hurry. Anything wrong?"

"I was trying to get away from a minibus. They were having a face off with my daughter."

"Really?" says the officer.

"It's true!" I yell. "They stole my new super-fish-face. You should get them for that. That's stealing you know!"

"They stole your face?" The policeman shakes his head.

"Yeah, it looks like this just in case you see it." I pull a super-fish-face at the policeman.

"Stop it, Lisa," Mum moans.

"I'll make a note of that," says the policeman. He writes out a speeding fine for Dad and then drives off. Dad looks very unhappy.

I see the minibus. It has turned around and is coming back towards us. "Look Dad! Here they come."

"Fish face!" yells Ben.

Ace goes crazy. He climbs over all of us into the front seat. He's up on the dash pulling doggie funny faces at the bus.

"Calm down!" yells Dad. Ace is squashing Dad right up against the door.

"Get off me!" says Chloe, covering her face from Ace's thrashing tail.

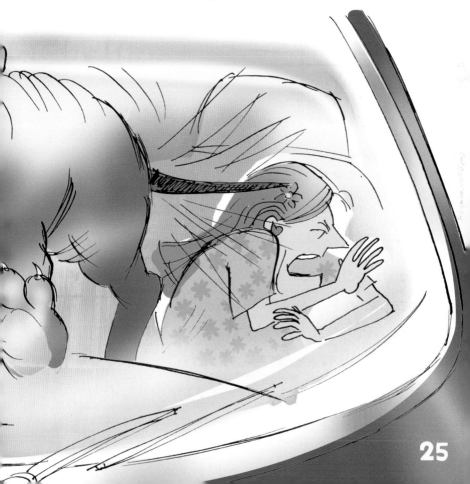

"Do something about him!' cries Mum to me.

I climb into the front to try and calm Ace down. Ben tries grabbing Ace's tail. The people in the bus think we are facing them off. All our faces are against the window. Suddenly the bus speeds off.

"We won the face off!" I cry.

We pile out of the car, except for Dad. He is still pressed up against the window, his face squished, eyes closed and his fingers in his ears. An old man walks out of a bus shelter yelling and waving a stick. He looks angry.

"He must think Dad's pulling a face at him," I say. Mum and Chloe pull Dad away from the window.

The old man looks at Dad. "It would look better if you did it like this." He puffs out his lips, crosses his eyes and wiggles his ears.

Ben bursts out laughing. Dad, Mum and Chloe are speechless.

"Awesome!" I say.

The old man looks pleased. "I think the people in the bus thought so! Did you see how fast they sped off?"

"You pulled the winning face?" I gasp.

The old man gives a toothless grin and screws up his face. "What's a face for, if it can't be funny, hey?"

I could learn a lot from this man. "Need a lift?" I ask. "You can have the back seat."

Glossary

attitude
tough, energetic style

busted
caught

dash (dashboard)
panel of instruments in a car

drools
slobber flows from mouth
without stopping

on a roll
to keep succeeding at
something

slobber
liquid from mouth

speechless
unable to speak due to surprise

speeding fine
money a driver pays for
travelling too fast

sprinting
running fast over a short
distance

weaves
moves from side to side to
pass things in the way

Lisa Thompson

When I get really nervous I can't stop laughing. Sometimes it can be very embarrassing. Imagine having a bad case of the giggles at these moments.

1. You're waiting to see the principal.
2. You're about to do a really important test.
3. You're standing on the edge of a really high diving board.
4. It's up to you to shoot the winning goal at netball.
5. You're standing in front of the whole school at assembly.

I've laughed in so many wrong places it's (almost) not funny! Hehehehehhahahah. (See what I mean?)

John Yahyeh

Contents

Chapter 1

The Face Pulling Seat

"I'm up the back!" I yell sprinting to the car.
I whiz past my sister, Chloe and fly past Mum
and my little brother, Ben. I get to the car
first, jump over the middle seat and climb
into the back. I've made it! I'm first!

"Excellent!" I say. The best seat is mine.
You can't beat the back seat for pulling
funny faces.

Three big windows — one each side and the big, back one. "It's all mine for the next six hours, all the way to Nana's," I beam to myself.

"Get out, Lisa!" demands Chloe. "You know Mum and Dad like you to sit in the middle, where they can keep an eye on you."

"Not this time!" I say. "This trip, I'm in the back to keep Ace company."

"Oh, we're not taking the dog!" cries Chloe.

"Yep!" I answer happily. "Ace and I are going to have heaps of fun in the back."

Dad lifts the back door and the dog leaps in.
Dad gets a tail whack in the head as he tries
to make Ace sit. Ace gives me a big, sloppy
kiss and slobber drools down onto my seat.

"That's disgusting!" yells Chloe.

"Bet you don't want to sit here now!" I laugh.

"Clean it off!" orders Mum, passing me a
hanky as she buckles Ben in. "Lisa, you and
Chloe will have to swap halfway. That way you
both get a turn in the back seat. Now move
over and buckle up."

"Drats!" I say under my breath. Mum has just
halved my face-pulling time.

We head out the driveway and into traffic. I see a taxi and pull my first face. I squish my face onto the window, blow up my cheeks and poke out my tongue. It takes a while for the taxi driver to notice me. He does a double take. Then he starts laughing and honks his horn. I'm off to a great start.

Chapter 2

On a Roll

I do my stuck-in-the-door-face to a bus. I cover my face with my hands and poke my tongue through my fingers. Ace and I do doggy faces to a mini-van and I do a monster face to a tow truck. I am on a roll.

It's time to give my new super-fish-face a go.
It's a fish face with attitude. Dad changes
lanes and I see my latest audience. It's a
minibus with a sign saying 'Happy Village Sight
Seeing'. It's full of people taking a tour. Dad
drives in front of the bus and I do my new
fish face.

The bus driver starts laughing. He changes lanes. I bet he's in the bus saying, "OK folks, if you look out of your right window you will see the best, funny face ever!"

Everyone on the bus is looking at me. Some are laughing, others are waving, taking photos or clapping. They are going wild! I knew this face was a winner!